A Bible Study on

ESSENTIALS OF

Francis M. Cosgrove, Jr.

NAVPRESS
A MINISTRY OF THE NAVIGATORS
P.O. Box 20, Colorado Springs, Colorado 80901

The Navigators is an international,
evangelical Christian organization.
Jesus Christ gave his followers the
Great Commission to go and make
disciples (Matthew 28:19). The aim
of The Navigators is to help fulfill
that commission by multiplying
laborers for Christ in every nation.

NavPress is the publishing ministry
of The Navigators. NavPress publications are tools to help Christians
grow. Although publications alone
cannot make disciples or change
lives, they can help believers learn
biblical discipleship, and apply what
they learn to their lives and
ministries.

Scripture quotations are from the
New International Version, © 1978
by the New York International Bible
Society.

Printed in the United States of
    America

CONTENTS

BEFORE YOU BEGIN

This Bible study has been written to accompany my book *Essentials of Discipleship*. Both were written to give you a comprehensive look at the basics of becoming a disciple of Jesus Christ. My purpose is to help you discover realistic goals for your development as a disciple.

Discipleship is clearly taught in Scripture. Christ's mandate to deny ourself, take up our cross daily, and follow him must be faced by every person who has trusted him as Savior (see Luke 9:23). The study leads you to search the Scriptures and develop your own understanding and convictions about discipleship.

This study can be used effectively in several ways:

Individual study. Set a consistent pace, such as one lesson a week for twelve weeks. Complete the study first, so that God's word becomes the foundation of your convictions. Each lesson will personalize for you the biblical teaching on the essentials of discipleship. Then read the corresponding chapter in *Essentials of Discipleship*.

Group discussion. The best way to appropriate these truths practically and to build one's own convictions is in a group setting. Do the study individually, then meet with a group of six to ten people and discuss what each one has gained in his own study. This approach will give you input from others who have prayerfully studied the material.

Class sessions. This material can also be used in a larger, more structured group such as a Sunday school class. The book could serve as the text and this study as the workbook that each class member would complete before coming to each session.

Each lesson includes:

*A Scripture Memory Assignment. It will take effort to memorize and review the verses, but meditating on them will help impress in your life the lessons you are learning.

*A Personal Project. You will especially enjoy these practical assignments on each topic. The Bible should not be studied only for the sake of knowledge; it should be applied to life. Each of the topics in the study is vital to a man or woman who wants to be Jesus' disciple, so application of each teaching must be made to life. This study should help you apply these scriptural truths so that you begin to match the profile of a disciple.

Guidelines for Group Discussion

The format for using this Bible study in a group is simple. The group members first answer the questions in a lesson individually at home, and then discuss their responses with each other when they meet together, which is usually once a week.

If you are the discussion leader for such a group, the material on the following pages will help you guide the group in an edifying time of fellowship centered on God's word.

BEFORE THE DISCUSSION
As the group leader, your most important preparation for each session is prayer. You will want to make your prayer requests personal, of course, but here are a few suggestions:

- Pray that everyone in the group will complete the lesson preparation, and will attend the discussion. Ask God to allow them to feel the freedom to honestly share their thoughts, and to make a significant contribution to the discussion.
- Ask God to give each one new understanding and practical applications from the Scriptures as you

5

talk. Pray that the unique needs of each person will be met in this way.

•Pray that you, as the leader, will know the Holy Spirit's guidance in exercising patience, acceptance, sensitivity, and wisdom. Pray for an atmosphere of genuine love in the group, with each member being honestly open to learning and change.

•Pray that as a result of your study and discussion, all of you will obey the Lord more closely and will more clearly demonstrate Christ's presence in your life.

After prayer, the next most important aspect of your preparation is to be thoroughly familiar with the lesson you're discussing. Make sure you have answered all the questions and have read the leader's material.

GETTING UNDER WAY

As the leader, take charge in an inoffensive way. The group is looking to you for leadership, and you should provide it. Work toward having a relaxed and open atmosphere. This may not come quickly, so be especially friendly at first, and communicate to the group that all of you are learning together.

You may want to experiment with various methods for discussing the study material. One simple approach is to discuss it question by question. You can go around the group in order, with the first person giving his answer to Question 1 (followed by a little discussion), the second person answering Question 2, and so on. Or, anyone in the group could answer each question as you come to it (the leader saying something such as "Who would like to take Question 5 for us?"). The question-by-question approach can be a good way to get young Christians started in Bible study discussion. The obvious structure gives them a sense of confidence, and they can see where the discussion is going.

The key to a more interesting and helpful discussion is good questions. These should challenge the group to look more closely at the subject and Scripture passage you are discussing. Suggested questions are included for each lesson in the Bible study. However, you will probably want to write some of your own as well. Having a good supply to choose from will help you quickly launch the discussion and keep it going in the right direction.

These guidelines will also help:

Asking questions

1. Make sure your questions are conversational.
2. Don't be afraid of silence after asking a question. Give everyone time to think.
3. Ask only one question at a time.
4. Don't ask questions which can be answered yes or no. This will hinder the discussion. Try beginning all your questions with "who," "what," "where," "when," "why," or "how."
5. Ask "What do you think?" occasionally to keep the discussion from seeming pressured or unnatural, since there is no such thing as a wrong answer to such a question. The person answering has freedom to simply give his viewpoint.
6. Remember that the Scriptures are the source of truth. Often you may want to look up together and read aloud the verses listed for the study questions as you discuss your answers.

Other discussion

1. Summarize frequently. Help the group see the direction of the discussion.
2. Allow time for adequate discussion of the application questions in each lesson. Your goal in Bible study is not, of course, to have something to discuss, but to change your life.
3. Allow adequate discussion also of the suggested special projects. Talk about how these can be adapted and implemented by everyone in the group.

General reminders

1. Your own attitude is a key factor in the group's enthusiasm. Develop a genuine interest in each person's remarks, and expect to learn from them.
2. Concentrate on developing acceptance and concern in the group. Avoid a businesslike atmosphere.
3. Participate in the discussion as a member of the group. Don't be either a lecturer or a silent observer.

4. Your total discussion time should probably not exceed ninety minutes, and one hour might be best. Start and end on time. Remember to close in group prayer.

You'll want to review these lists often.

AFTER THE DISCUSSION

Use these self-evaluation questions after each session to improve your leadership the next time:

1. Did you discuss the major points in the chapter?
2. Did you have enough prepared questions to properly guide the discussion?
3. Did you know your material well enough to have freedom in leading?
4. Did you keep the discussion from wandering?
5. Did everyone participate in the discussion?
6. Was the discussion practical?
7. Did you begin and end on time?

WHAT IS A DISCIPLE?

Scripture Memory Assignment: Matthew 28:18-20

1. What is a disciple? Read Matthew 5:1-2 and 11:1, and John 8:31. You may want to consult a dictionary as well.

   _____

   _____

   _____

2. Read each pair of verses: 2 Corinthians 9:7 and Acts 11:29, Luke 9:5 and Acts 13:49-51, and Matthew 16:24 and Acts 20:22-24. How should a disciple respond to instruction?

   _____

   _____

   _____

   _____

3. Read each of the following verses and tell what instruction or essential for discipleship you see in them.

As you do, make note of any reactions or thoughts you have about each essential. Pray about the passages which were most challenging to you.

Proverbs 9:10

_____

_____

_____

Matthew 6:33

_____

_____

_____

Titus 2:11-14

_____

_____

_____

Mark 1:35

_____

_____

_____

Acts 17:11

_____

_____

Acts 1:8

_____

_____

_____

Hebrews 10:24-25

_____

_____

_____

Ephesians 4:1-3

_____

_____

_____

Mark 10:42-45

_____

_____

_____

Malachi 3:10-11

_____

_____

_____

Galatians 5:22-23

_____

_____

_____

4. a. Read Luke 6:40. Who will a mature disciple resemble?

_____

   b. Can you think of one or more ways in which you are beginning to resemble Jesus Christ? Describe them.

_____

_____

_____

5. Read John 13:34-35. What shows that we are a disciple of Christ?

_____

_____

_____

6. In order to develop as a disciple, certain qualities are necessary. Which quality is suggested by each of the following verses?

Luke 9
verses 23-25

_____

verse 26

_____

verses 46-48

_____

verses 61-62

_____

Luke 14
verses 8-11

_____

verses 12-14

_____

verses 28-33

_____

verses 34-35

_____

7. a. Which of the qualities you listed is easy for you to display?

_____

   b. Which quality is difficult to display?

_____

8. Read Luke 9:23 and 14:27. What does it mean to "take up" or "carry" your cross? Think of Jesus as he carried

his own cross before he was crucified.

_____

_____

_____

_____

9. What are the blessings of discipleship listed in Luke
   6:20-23?

_____

_____

_____

10. Read Luke 12:27-31.

   a. What should be our priority from day to day?

   _____

   _____

   b. What should be our attitude about daily
      necessities?

   _____

   _____

   c. Why should that be our attitude?

   _____

   _____

_____

_____

11. Read Matthew 28:18-20.

    a. What is our responsibility to the nations of the world?

_____

_____

_____

    b. What assurance should enable us to help carry out the Great Commission?

_____

_____

12. Why does it take a disciple to make other disciples?

_____

_____

_____

13. Do you know a Christian you would call a disciple? Why do you think of that person as a disciple?

_____

_____

_____

_____

Personal Project: Look again at Question 7. Make specific plans to strengthen that quality in your life which is difficult to put into practice.

_____

_____

_____

_____

_____

_____

Questions for Group Discussion
The purpose of this lesson is to begin to understand what a disciple is, and to realize that every Christian should be growing toward being a disciple.

1. Take a few minutes to review the Scripture memory assignment. You may prefer to do so in pairs, one person listening and the other repeating the verse.
2. Discuss your answers to Question 1. What important point is made in John 8:31? How does that relate to growth as a disciple?
3. To begin discussion of Question 3, have several people share their responses. Were there any passages you did not understand? Would you add any essentials to the list? If so, what? Can you suggest some verses to support that essential? How do these essentials compare with the profile of a disciple in Chapter 1 of *Essentials of Discipleship*? If you felt you needed to grow in every way, which essential might be the best place to begin? Why?
4. Share responses to Question 4. Who should a disciple learn from?
5. Before discussing Question 5, have someone read John 13:34-35. How can Christians love one another in a

16

way that is different from non-Christians? Why do you think Jesus spoke about love as he was telling the disciples about his coming absence?

6. As Question 6 is discussed, try to define each quality mentioned. How do you think each quality relates to discipleship? Are any of these qualities more important than others? If so, which ones?

7. Discuss Question 10. We may be anxious or worried about our needs. What advice is given in Philippians 4:6-7?

8. The passage for Question 11 gives a Christian a purpose in life. What do you think "making disciples" means?

9. Share responses to Question 12. Could someone become a disciple without the help of another disciple?

10. Discuss Question 13. Would you say every Christian is a disciple? Should every Christian strive to become a disciple?

11. Spend some time discussing the personal project suggested for this lesson. Some of those in the group may need practical suggestions as to how they could strengthen a particular quality in their lives.

12. Have a closing period of group prayer for the personal project and each person's plans.

NOTES FROM YOUR GROUP DISCUSSION

THE DISCIPLE
IS A LEARNER

Review Matthew 28:18-20, and check here __ after quoting it correctly from memory.

Scripture Memory Assignment: Proverbs 1:5, 7

1. What concept does the Apostle Paul communicate in 1 Thessalonians 4:8?

_____

_____

_____

_____

2. Read John 6:60-66. Why did many disciples stop following Jesus?

_____

_____

_____

_____

3. One way we can learn is by following the example of others. According to 1 Corinthians 11:1 and Hebrews 13:7, whom should we follow?

_____

_____

4. What will take place over a period of time as we follow Christ's example? Summarize 2 Corinthians 3:18.

_____

_____

_____

_____

What example does Christ set for us in Mark 7:37?

_____

_____

5. What is one thing a follower of Christ will learn? Read Matthew 4:19.

_____

_____

6. According to Hebrews 13:17, what kind of relationship are we to have with our leaders? What does that have to do with being a learner?

_____

_____

_____

_____

_____

7. According to Philippians 4:9, what are we to do concerning what we have learned?

_____

_____

8. What have you learned about living the Christian life which you have not yet put into practice? What do you plan to do about it?

_____

_____

_____

9. Write out what these passages teach about being a learner and responding to correction.

Proverbs 1:29-33

_____

_____

_____

Proverbs 9:8-10

_____

_____

Proverbs 10:17

_____

_____

_____

Proverbs 13:18

_____

_____

_____

10. Read Luke 10:25-29.

a. What was the reaction of the lawyer to Jesus' instruction concerning eternal life?

_____

_____

_____

_____

b. Give an illustration from your own life or something you have observed that is similar to the lawyer's response.

_____

_____

_____

_____

11. Write down areas of your life in which you have no difficulty being a learner, and areas in which you have been closed to learning.

_____

_____

_____

_____

_____

12. What activity are you, or could you be, involved in that will help you be a diligent learner?

_____

_____

_____

Personal Project: Make a list of things you believe you need to learn as a disciple. Then find a person, perhaps in your church fellowship or study group, from whom you can learn. Make arrangements to start meeting with that person for the purpose of instruction.

_____

_____

_____

_____

_____

Questions for Group Discussion
The purpose of this lesson is to begin learning or continue
learning as a disciple of Jesus Christ. Learning is a major
activity of life. Being a Christian adds another dimension
to being a learner. We must grow and mature spiritually
as well as acquire skills and knowledge for day-to-day
living.

1. Spend a few minutes reviewing the Scripture memory
   assignment for the lesson. If some in the group have
   memorized an additional verse or passage of their own
   choosing, ask them to share it and their reason for
   selecting it.
2. As you read 1 Thessalonians 4:8 for Question 1, did
   you become aware of a thought which should be a
   matter of prayer for you, either confession or praise or
   petition?
3. The Scripture passage for Question 2 (John 6:60-66)
   concerns difficult teachings. In what way do you think
   they are difficult—being able to understand them, or
   being willing to apply them?
4. Questions 3 and 4 point to Christ as our example.
   Read 1 Thessalonians 1:6-7, then describe what took
   place as the Thessalonians imitated Paul and Christ.
5. Read the verse for Question 7 again (Philippians 4:9).
   How does the second sentence in the verse relate to the
   first sentence?
6. If someone is willing to share their answer to Question
   8, ask them to also share the reason they have pre-
   viously not applied what they learned.
7. In your discussion of Question 9 include some
   thoughts on the relationship of fear and wisdom.
   What is fear of the Lord?
8. Discuss responses to Question 10. What are some
   ways you have responded to instruction in the past?
   Give both a positive and a negative example.
9. Discuss the personal project. Did God impress one
   thought on your mind concerning your responsibility
   as a learner? How will you follow through?
10. Close the discussion with a time of prayer.

NOTES FROM YOUR GROUP DISCUSSION

THE LORDSHIP
OF JESUS CHRIST

Review the following verses, and check them off after quoting them correctly from memory.

Matthew 28:18-20 ___   Proverbs 1:5, 7 ___

Scripture Memory Assignment: Jeremiah 29:11

1. Write a definition of *lordship* using a dictionary.

_____

_____

_____

2. Use the following verses to write your own definition of the lordship of Jesus Christ: Luke 6:46, John 13:13, 2 Corinthians 5:15.

_____

_____

_____

_____

3. How does your biblical definition of Christ's lordship compare to the dictionary definition?

_____

_____

_____

_____

4. Which phrase in the Lord's Prayer in Matthew 6:9-13 emphasizes your submission to Christ's lordship? Explain your choice.

_____

_____

_____

_____

5. Read Colossians 1:15-18.

   a. What are some things over which Christ is Lord?

   _____

   _____

   _____

   b. Why is he Lord over these things?

   _____

   _____

   _____

26

c. If Christ is your creator, what other position should he also have in your life?

_____

_____

6. Read Acts 2:36 and Philippians 2:8-11. In your own words, what do those verses tell us about Jesus' position in our life?

_____

_____

_____

7. Which statement applies to you? Put a line under it.

a. I have not made a conscious decision concerning lordship.

b. I have experienced some victories and some defeats in submitting to Christ's lordship.

c. I submit to Christ's lordship because I want his best for my life.

8. Do you agree with the statement, "Jesus Christ is either Lord of all, or he is not Lord at all"? Explain your answer.

_____

_____

_____

_____

9. Read Matthew 6:24.

   a. Why is it impossible to serve two masters at the same time?

   _____

   _____

   _____

   _____

   b. What are the two masters mentioned in the verse?

   _____

   _____

   c. What are some other worldly masters?

   _____

   _____

   _____

   d. Can you recall a time when you tried to serve two masters? What was the result?

   _____

   _____

   _____

   _____

   _____

e. Describe a choice you are facing which involves Christ's lordship. It may be a decision you make once in a lifetime, or once a day.

_____

_____

_____

_____

_____

10. According to Romans 7:21-23, why is submitting to the lordship of Christ so difficult for many Christians?

_____

_____

_____

11. As sinners, we are always struggling with lordship. What area of your life could you submit to Christ as a learning experience?

_____

_____

_____

How could Jeremiah 29:11 help you?

_____

_____

_____

12. Has this lesson changed your understanding of lordship and your response to it? How?

_____

_____

_____

_____

Personal Project: List at least six areas of your life in which obedience to Christ should be a consideration. In which of those areas are you having a struggle? Write out a practical way you plan to deal with one of them.

_____

_____

_____

_____

_____

_____

_____

Questions for Group Discussion
Christians have a responsibility to submit to Christ's lordship after they have accepted his salvation. This lesson will reveal that lordship involves a daily battle. The areas of battle are discussed, as well as the blessings of experiencing Christ's lordship.

1. Begin the study by spending a few minutes reviewing the Scripture memory assignment.
2. Compare answers to Question 2. Does lordship leave

any room for a person to make his own decisions? Discuss the choices made for Question 4.

3. According to Matthew 6:9-13, is Christ Lord without any question?

4. Share answers to Question 5. Can we say that Christ is our Lord even if we sometimes fail to obey him?

5. Discuss responses to Question 6. How often do you have to ask Christ to be your Savior? How often do you have to ask him to be your Lord? Would Christ have to be our Savior if we always obeyed him as our Lord? Explain your answer.

6. Discuss responses to Question 8.

7. Before discussing Question 9, ask at what point does something become the master of your life?

8. Share responses to Question 10. For what reasons given in Chapter 3 of *Essentials of Discipleship* do many people fail to acknowledge Christ's lordship? Can you suggest any other reasons?

9. Discuss responses to Question 11 if some of those present are willing to share. Turn to the stages of obedience that are discussed on pages 47-48 in *Essentials of Discipleship*. At which stage of obedience do you find yourself? Does it vary depending on the area of your life that is involved? What steps could you take to move to the next stage?

   Read Psalm 37:4. What does it mean to "delight yourself in the Lord"? What attitude on our part triggers God's response on our behalf?

10. Talk about Question 12. Can you recall a difficult lordship decision you made and the blessing you experienced as a result?

11. As responses to the personal project are shared, compile a list of areas of life which should be submitted to Christ. Get suggestions from several, if not all, of those in the group. Try to include ideas such as giving thanks in all things, an issue which touches all the areas of a person's life. Perhaps some in the group would be willing to share a personal struggle, and receive some practical suggestions for achieving victory.

NOTES FROM YOUR GROUP DISCUSSION

PURITY
OF LIFE

Review the following verses, and check them off after quoting them correctly from memory.

Matthew 28:18-20 ___   Proverbs 1:5, 7 ___
Jeremiah 29:11 ___

Scripture Memory Assignment: Titus 2:11-12

1. Why is purity of life a vital necessity according to 1 Thessalonians 4:7?

_____

_____

_____

_____

2. Read Titus 2:11-14.

   a. Describe the kind of life we should live.

   _____

   _____

_____

_____

_____

b. How is Christ's death related to our purity?

_____

_____

_____

_____

_____

3. Read Galatians 5:16-18.

a. Why is the maintenance of godliness so difficult?

_____

_____

_____

_____

_____

b. What is our source of strength to overcome the old nature?

_____

_____

_____

4. List the goals of the new nature, as found in Ephesians 4:22-5:5.

_____

_____

_____

_____

_____

_____

5. From Colossians 3:5-10 and Galatians 5:19-21, list impure habits of the old nature that should be discarded.

_____

_____

_____

_____

_____

_____

6. Read 1 Corinthians 6:18-20.

a. How is sexual sin different from all others?

_____

_____

_____

_____

b. Why shouldn't we sin against our own body?

_____

_____

_____

_____

7. Review your responses to Questions 4 through 6. Is there at least one area in which you have not been too concerned about purity, or perhaps even consciously rejected it?

_____

_____

Why has this been your attitude?

_____

_____

_____

_____

8. Read 1 John 1:8-10. How should John's teaching be applied in our battle for purity?

_____

_____

_____

_____

9. Paraphrase each instruction you find in Proverbs 4:23-27.

_____

_____

_____

_____

_____

_____

Can a person lead an impure life if he or she is guided by wisdom? Explain your answer.

_____

_____

_____

_____

Personal Project: Read Proverbs 18:24 and 27:17. Look for someone with whom you can share your struggle for purity. Then agree to encourage and help one another in practical ways to win the battle.

Questions for Group Discussion
As a result of doing this lesson, each person will realize that God wants him to live a pure life. He or she will discover that the battle for purity goes on in the life of each Christian. Purity should be achieved in every area of life by making specific plans to reach that goal.

1. Take a few minutes to review the Scripture memory assignment.

2. Share responses to Question 1. What are some words other than *pure* that describe the life we are to live?
3. Discuss Question 2. What are some practical steps that can be taken to say no to ungodliness? Which step is the hardest?
4. For Questions 4 and 5, be sure everyone has a good idea of what each goal and habit means. Perhaps someone in the group has achieved victory over an old habit and would share how they did so.
5. Answer Question 6. Is sexual sin a worse sin than others? What thought from the passage could be a source of strength in times of struggle?
6. Share responses to Question 7. Compile a group list of areas in which purity should be maintained. Is it possible to be sexually impure through secondhand means, such as what you read? What are some other examples?
7. Discuss Question 8. How can 1 John 1:8-10 be used as the basis for specific, personal prayer?
8. Read Proverbs 18:24 and 27:17. How do these verses apply to the personal project? In what other ways can they be applied to life?
9. Spend a few minutes praying. Include any personal struggles which people in the group have been willing to share.

NOTES FROM YOUR GROUP DISCUSSION

PRAYER
AND DEVOTIONS

Review the following verses, and check them off after quoting them correctly from memory.

Matthew 28:18-20 ___   Proverbs 1:5, 7 ___
Jeremiah 29:11 ___   Titus 2:11-12 ___

Scripture Memory Assignment: Psalm 27:8

1. Describe the devotional life of Jesus, using Matthew 14:23, Mark 1:35, and Luke 5:16.

_____

_____

_____

_____

2. Why is prayer a vital necessity for our life? Read Psalm 38:18 and 62:8.

_____

_____

_____

3. In Luke 11:2-4, Jesus taught his disciples how to pray. For each aspect of prayer given below, copy a phrase from the passage in Luke.

adoration or praise

_____

_____

confession

_____

_____

petition or intercession

_____

_____

4. Another important element of prayer is mentioned in Ephesians 5:20. What is it and how should it be applied?

_____

_____

_____

5. Petition should include some requests for others. Read 1 Samuel 12:23. How important is it that we pray for others?

_____

_____

_____

6. For what reason, given in James 5:16, should we pray for others?

_____

_____

_____

_____

7. Why must we confess our sins before we pray for others?

_____

_____

_____

_____

8. What step could you take to improve your approach to praying for others?

_____

_____

_____

_____

9. Read 1 Thessalonians 5:17. How can we apply this instruction?

_____

_____

_____

10. Paraphrase the instructions for prayer that are found in James 1:5.

_____

_____

11. What do you need wisdom for? Have you asked God to supply it?

_____

_____

_____

12. Read James 1:6-7.

a. What condition does God establish for answered prayer?

_____

_____

b. What should we believe?

_____

_____

_____

13. What can you learn from the example of David in Psalm 5:3, 63:1-8, and 143:8?

_____

_____

_____

Personal Project: Plan your prayer time for the next seven days. Write down a different item of adoration or praise, confession, petition or intercession, and thanksgiving for each day. After seven days, try to write some new ideas for another seven days. See how long you can do this.

_____

_____

_____

_____

_____

_____

_____

Questions for Group Discussion
The purpose of this lesson is to motivate each person to develop a workable, consistent quiet time. The lesson covers the example Christ set and principles for an effective, rewarding devotional life.

1. Begin with the Scripture memory assignment.
2. Answer Question 1. What was your reaction as you thought about Christ's habit of prayer?
3. Share your responses to Question 2. Do you think God will be surprised by something we say, whether it be confession, a feeling or desire or request? Can anything we say to God sever our relationship with him?
4. Thoroughly discuss Questions 3 and 4. How can you maintain balance in your prayers to avoid spending all your time on petition?

   Read Hebrews 13:15. Why do you think praise is a sacrifice? Turn to 1 Thessalonians 5:18. How much importance does God place on giving thanks?

5. Share responses to Questions 5, 6, 7, and 8, which are concerned with praying for others. What has helped you increase your effectiveness in praying for others? What experiences have you had or been aware of that relate to praying for others?
6. Discuss answers to Question 9. Should we pray about something frequently if we are motivated to do so by anxiety?
7. Have several people share their paraphrase of James 1:5 (Question 10). Share personal experiences concerning a need for wisdom which God supplied. Is a request for wisdom the same as a request for guidance?
8. Provide an opportunity for those who are willing to share their response to Question 11.
9. Discuss Question 12. What are some causes of doubt that God will answer our prayer? How can we overcome such doubts?
10. Answer Question 13.
11. As you discuss the personal project, have group members share two of their most helpful ideas for planning a weekly prayer list.
12. Encourage those who pray at the close of the study to include expressions of adoration, confession, thanksgiving, and petition.

NOTES FROM YOUR GROUP DISCUSSION

THE IMPORTANCE
OF THE BIBLE

Review the following verses, and check them off after quoting them correctly from memory.

Matthew 28:18-20 ___   Proverbs 1:5, 7 ___
Jeremiah 29:11 ___   Titus 2:11-12 ___
Psalm 27:8 ___

Scripture Memory Assignment: 2 Timothy 3:16-17

1. Describe your present intake of the word of God: what you're doing, how you're doing it, and how much time it takes. Consider hearing, reading, studying, memorizing, and meditating on God's word.

_____

_____

_____

_____

_____

_____

_____

2. Which activity seems most beneficial to you? Which is the most difficult? Why?

_____

_____

_____

_____

_____

3. Read Job 23:12 and Jeremiah 15:16.

    a. Describe the attitude of these two men toward God's word.

_____

_____

_____

_____

_____

    b. How can you develop a greater desire for God's word?

_____

_____

_____

_____

_____

4. According to Matthew 22:29, what risk do we take if we don't know the Scriptures?

_____

_____

_____

What is the relationship of knowledge of the Scriptures and knowledge of the power of God?

_____

_____

_____

5. Study 2 Timothy 3:16-17.

a. What four purposes does Scripture fulfill?

_____

_____

_____

b. Write a definition for each purpose so that the differences are clear. You may wish to use a Bible dictionary.

_____

_____

_____

_____

_____

_____

_____

_____

6. What goal concerning God's word is established for a disciple in 2 Timothy 2:15?

_____

_____

_____

_____

7. Describe a systematic approach you could follow to grow and increase your knowledge of the Scriptures and skill in applying them.

_____

_____

_____

_____

_____

_____

8. Read Acts 17:11.

   a. What example did the Bereans give us?

_____

_____

b. How could you apply that example to your intake of God's word?

_____

_____

_____

_____

_____

9. Read Colossians 3:16. What activities in your spiritual life should be based on knowledge of God's word?

_____

_____

_____

Personal Project: Choose one of the following activities: hearing, reading, studying, memorizing, or meditating on the Scriptures. Plan how to go about it more consistently and effectively.

_____

_____

_____

_____

_____

_____

_____

_____

_____

Questions for Group Discussion
As a result of this lesson, each person in the group should have a deeper commitment to the Bible as the word of God. It is necessary for teaching, rebuke, correction, and training in righteousness. We can take in the word of God by hearing, reading, studying, memorizing, and meditating on it.

1. Review the Scripture memory assignment, including verses other than the suggested passage, if some in the group have chosen others to memorize.
2. What are the five suggested means of intake of the word of God (Question 1)? Can you suggest any others? What does it mean to meditate on Scripture?
3. Share responses to Question 2.
4. Answer Question 3, part a. Share responses to part b. What will come first, the desire for God's word or activities which are centered in the word?
5. Discuss both parts of Question 4. Can you think of ways we might suffer because of a lack of knowledge of God's word? Has a particular verse or passage been instrumental in helping you make a decision?
6. Answer Question 5, part a. Share responses to part b. Can you think of a verse or passage which accomplishes each purpose? Share responses to part c. If we were as open to teaching and training from the Scriptures as we should be, would we still need the rebuke and correction it also provides?
7. Discuss Question 6. How could you pace yourself toward that goal?
8. For Question 7, give those who want to, an opportunity to share their thoughts and ask questions.
9. Respond to Question 8. What should be your attitude as you consider what someone has taught?

10. Share responses to Question 9. What can be the result when teaching and admonishing are done without being based in the word of God?
11. Encourage those in the group to share their plans for the personal project. Some may share plans they have already followed with success.
12. Spend the closing minutes in prayer.

NOTES FROM YOUR GROUP DISCUSSION

THE PRIMACY
OF EVANGELISM

Review the following verses, and check them off after quoting them correctly from memory.

Matthew 28:18-20 ___   Proverbs 1:5, 7 ___
Jeremiah 29:11 ___   Titus 2:11-12 ___
Psalm 27:8 ___   2 Timothy 3:16-17 ___

Scripture Memory Assignment: 1 Corinthians 9:16

1. According to John 15:16, what is God's plan for us?

_____

_____

_____

2. What are some reasons why you have shared the gospel sometimes but not at other times?

_____

_____

_____

_____

3. The Great Commission is recorded in all four Gospels
   and in Acts. What are the important points of each
   verse or passage?

   Matthew 28:18-20

   _____

   _____

   _____

   _____

   Mark 16:15

   _____

   _____

   _____

   Luke 24:46-48

   _____

   _____

   _____

   _____

   John 20:21

   _____

   _____

   _____

Acts 1:8

_____

_____

_____

4. How do your present activities and circumstances fit into the Great Commission?

_____

_____

_____

_____

_____

Do you see the need for a change in your life in order to be involved in the Great Commission? What might that change be?

_____

_____

_____

_____

5. Read Acts 5:42, 14:21-23, and 1 Peter 3:15. On this page and the next page, write a brief paragraph on what you think is involved in evangelism.

_____

_____

_____

_____

_____

_____

_____

_____

_____

_____

6. Write your personal testimony as briefly as possible.

_____

_____

_____

_____

_____

_____

_____

_____

_____

7. Use these verses to tell why you have the hope of eternal life: 1 Timothy 2:5, Romans 3:23, 2 Thessalonians 1:8-9, 1 Peter 3:18, John 1:12, 1 John 5:11-12.

_____

_____

_____

_____

_____

_____

_____

8. What specific steps can you take to increase your opportunities to witness?

_____

_____

_____

_____

_____

Personal Project: Ask God to guide you in choosing someone you are acquainted with to whom you can witness. Pray also that he will help you make some plans to reach that person.

_____

_____

_____

_____

_____

_____

_____

Questions for Group Discussion

The purpose of this lesson is to challenge those in the group to become effective witnesses for Jesus Christ. They will be encouraged by the example of the early Church. An important part of the lesson is to write out their testimonies and a brief explanation of the gospel.

1. Review the Scripture memory assignment.
2. Answer Question 1. What is your philosophy of witnessing? Have you seen John 15:16 fulfilled in your life and ministry?
3. Give an opportunity for those in the group who wish to, to respond to Question 2. Is it always right to witness to someone who is not a Christian?
4. Discuss Question 3. Use all the passages to summarize Jesus' teaching about the Great Commission.
5. Since Question 4 is for personal application, encourage response only if people are willing to do so. Suggest that this question might become a matter of prayer.
6. Discuss Question 5. Have you been involved in a structured evangelistic effort? Describe it. What were its strengths and weaknesses?
7. Those who grew up in a Christian environment and became Christians at an early age may have the most difficulty writing their testimonies (Question 6), since they think they don't have a dramatic one. Some suggestions from the group may help them develop an effective tool.
8. Share responses to Question 7. Are there some other

verses you would use as well as those suggested? What are they, and why do you prefer them? If you have had an opportunity to share your testimony and present the gospel to someone, how would you conclude the conversation? Recall the comments concerning reaping which were made in Chapter 7 of *Essentials of Discipleship*.
9. Discuss responses to Question 8.
10. Take time for questions or comments concerning the personal project.
11. Spend time praying that some point of discussion during the Bible study will be used in each person's life, and that God will prepare the hearts of those with whom some people in the study will share the gospel.

NOTES FROM YOUR GROUP DISCUSSION

THE CHURCH
AND BODY LIFE

Review the following verses, and check them off after quoting them correctly from memory.

Matthew 28:18-20 ___   Proverbs 1:5, 7 ___
Jeremiah 29:11 ___   Titus 2:11-12 ___
Psalm 27:8 ___   2 Timothy 3:16-17 ___
1 Corinthians 9:16 ___

Scripture Memory Assignment: 1 Thessalonians 5:12-13

1. According to the following passages from Acts, what characterized the early Church and caused it to grow?

   Acts 2:36-41

   _____

   _____

   Acts 2:42-47

   _____

   _____

   _____

   _____

Acts 3:16

_____

_____

Acts 4:20

_____

_____

Acts 4:24, 29-31

_____

_____

Acts 4:32-35

_____

_____

_____

Acts 5:41

_____

_____

Acts 6:3-7

_____

_____

_____

Acts 8:1,4

_____

_____

2. How can the church today learn from the early
   Church?

   _____

   _____

   _____

   _____

   _____

   _____

3. In what ways is the church important in the life of a
   disciple, according to each of these passages?

   Psalm 133:1

   _____

   _____

   _____

   Acts 16:5

   _____

   _____

   _____

1 Corinthians 12:12-27

_____

_____

_____

_____

_____

Colossians 1:15-18

_____

_____

_____

Hebrews 10:24-25

_____

_____

_____

4. What do you contribute to the life and ministry of
   your local church?

_____

_____

_____

_____

_____

What do you receive from your church?

_____

_____

_____

_____

_____

Do you think you should contribute more to your church? If so, what specifically could you do?

_____

_____

_____

_____

5. Read Ephesians 4:11-12.

   a. What responsibility do leaders have toward the people in the church?

   _____

   _____

   _____

   b. What is the goal of these leaders?

   _____

   _____

   _____

6. How are leaders to go about their task? Read Acts
   20:28, Titus 1:9, and 1 Peter 5:2-3.

   _____

   _____

   _____

   _____

   _____

   _____

7. What characterizes the life of a leader in the church?
   Make a list based on 1 Timothy 3:1-13, Titus 1:6-8,
   and 1 Peter 5:2-3.

   _____

   _____

   _____

   _____

   _____

   _____

   _____

   _____

   _____

Personal Project: Compare your life with the description of a church leader, whether or not you are one. Ask God to help you make an honest evaluation. Then act on the greatest need you see in your life.

_____

_____

_____

_____

_____

_____

_____

_____

Questions for Group Discussion
The purpose of this lesson is to understand that church is more than a Sunday morning ritual. It is the world-wide group of believers as well as a local congregation. Involvement in a church is not a matter of choice, but a God-given responsibility which may include a position of leadership over those in the fellowship.

1. Begin the study by spending a few minutes reviewing the Scripture memory assignment.
2. Discuss the responses to Questions 1 and 2. Have the differences between the early Church and present-day church been beneficial or a hindrance to growth?
3. Share responses to Question 3. In some passages you may be able to identify a way in which a disciple is important to the life of a church as well.
4. Question 4 is a personal application question. If those in the study represent several different churches, ask them to share unique means of involvement that are

going on in their church. Should a person do something in the church only if he or she has a motivating interest in it? Is it possible to be too involved in the activities of a church? What guidelines do you follow?

5. As Questions 5 and 6 are discussed, be sure those in the group have some understanding of what it means to build up the body of Christ. Read aloud Ephesians 4:13, which expresses the goal of all Christians.

6. Share answers to Question 7. Should a person in a position of leadership in the church be asked to give up that responsibility if his or her life does not measure up to God's standard?

7. Discuss the personal project. To what degree, if any, can the life of a church leader fall short of God's requirements for such a position?

8. Close the study of this lesson with prayer.

NOTES FROM YOUR GROUP DISCUSSION

CHRISTIAN FELLOWSHIP

Review the following verses, and check them off after quoting them correctly from memory.

Matthew 28:18-20 ___   Proverbs 1:5, 7 ___
Jeremiah 29:11 ___   Titus 2:11-12 ___
Psalm 27:8 ___   2 Timothy 3:16-17 ___
1 Corinthians 9:16 ___   1 Thessalonians 5:12-13 ___

Scripture Memory Assignment: 1 John 1:3

1. How would you define fellowship?

_____

_____

_____

2. Write a definition of *fellowship* using a Bible dictionary or encyclopedia.

_____

_____

_____

_____

3. Read 1 John 1:1-3. What is the basis for fellowship with other Christians?

_____

_____

_____

_____

4. Read John 17:23, Acts 4:32, and Ephesians 4:2-3. What must characterize the body of believers, and why?

_____

_____

_____

_____

_____

5. In Acts 2:42-47, how did the believers take part in fellowship with one another?

_____

_____

_____

_____

_____

6. Why is fellowship important according to each of the following verses?

Proverbs 13:20

_____

_____

_____

Proverbs 27:17

_____

_____

_____

_____

Ecclesiastes 4:9-10

_____

_____

_____

_____

Hebrews 3:12-13

_____

_____

_____

_____

7. Think of one area in your life for which you need encouragement, counsel, prayer support, or wisdom. Think of someone who would be a source of that kind of fellowship.

_____

_____

_____

_____

Is there someone in your fellowship who needs help? What could you do?

_____

_____

_____

_____

8. Write a brief summary of what should be found in biblical fellowship. Refer to your answers for Question 6.

_____

_____

_____

_____

_____

_____

9. How biblical is the fellowship in which you are active? Explain your answer.

_____

_____

_____

_____

Can that fellowship be improved? How?

_____

_____

_____

_____

_____

Personal Project: Think of at least one way that the entertaining you do in your home can be more like the biblical fellowship studied in this lesson.

_____

_____

_____

_____

_____

Questions for Group Discussion
This lesson will teach what biblical fellowship is. Many times what is called fellowship is simply a social event.

You will discuss principles and activities which are basic to Christian fellowship and discover that fellowship includes learning from others.

1. As you spend a few minutes reviewing the Scripture memory assignment, those who memorized an additional verse or passage might tell why they did so.
2. Have several in the group share their answers to Questions 1 and 2 so that you have as complete a definition of fellowship as possible. How, if at all, did your definition of fellowship differ from those definitions you found in other sources?
3. Read the passage for Question 3 (1 John 1:1-3) and discuss your answers. What was John referring to in verses 1 and 2? What is your responsibility concerning the furtherance of fellowship among Christians?
4. Discuss answers to Question 4. How would you define unity? Does it mean that there is no disagreement?
5. Share reasons why fellowship is important to every believer (Question 6). What effect could it have on a Christian if he or she had no fellowship? Consider Proverbs 13:20. What experience can you recall in which you received help from someone? Can fellowship sometimes be a difficult or painful experience?
6. Share responses to Question 7 and together summarize what true fellowship is. Then compare the group's description with that in Chapter 9 of *Essentials of Discipleship*.
7. For discussion of Question 9, share the positive qualities that characterize the fellowships of which those in the group are a part.
8. Some of those in the group may not have realized that their home can be a setting for fellowship, as suggested by the personal project. From the passages that were studied for this lesson, list some ways in which a home can be used for fellowship.
9. As you spend a few minutes in prayer at the end of the discussion, thank God for the many blessings of regular fellowship with other Christians.

NOTES FROM YOUR GROUP DISCUSSION

THE DISCIPLE
IS A SERVANT

Review the following verses, and check them off after quoting them correctly from memory.

Matthew 28:18-20 ___   Proverbs 1:5, 7 ___
Jeremiah 29:11 ___   Titus 2:11-12 ___
Psalm 27:8 ___   2 Timothy 3:16-17 ___
1 Corinthians 9:16 ___   1 Thessalonians 5:12-13 ___
1 John 1:3 ___

Scripture Memory Assignment: 2 Corinthians 4:5

1. What is your impression of the way in which Christians serve other Christians, as well as non-Christians?

_____

_____

_____

_____

_____

_____

_____

2. Have you consciously given much thought and planning to your responsibility to serve others? What do you believe have been your strengths and weaknesses as a servant in the past?

_____

_____

_____

_____

_____

3. Jesus was the greatest servant. What does his example teach us? See Mark 10:45, John 13:14-17, and Philippians 2:5-8.

_____

_____

_____

_____

_____

4. Read Mark 10:42-44 and Philippians 2:25-30. What do you believe is the biblical teaching about being servants?

_____

_____

_____

_____

5. What was Paul's attitude toward serving others? See 2 Corinthians 12:15.

_____

_____

_____

6. Paraphrase 2 Corinthians 4:5.

_____

_____

_____

Why should a Christian be a servant of others?

_____

_____

_____

_____

7. Describe the range of activities that a Christian can be involved in as a servant. Two examples are recorded in Acts 6:1-4 and 1 Thessalonians 2:8.

_____

_____

_____

_____

_____

8. Read Matthew 25:31-46. List at least five ways in which a disciple can serve Christ by meeting others' needs.

_____

_____

_____

_____

_____

9. What characteristics of a servant are encouraged in each verse or passage? Give an example of how each characteristic could meet a need in a Christian fellowship.

1 Samuel 22:14

_____

_____

_____

_____

2 Samuel 15:21

_____

_____

_____

_____

Ephesians 6:5

_____

_____

_____

_____

2 Timothy 2:24-25

_____

_____

_____

_____

Titus 2:9-10

_____

_____

_____

_____

10. Based on this lesson, what steps could you take to increase your effectiveness as a servant?

_____

_____

_____

_____

Personal Project: What are some specific ways in which you could serve a non-Christian you know so that you might have an opportunity to present the gospel? Make plans to carry out one of your ideas.

_____

_____

_____

_____

_____

Questions for Group Discussion
In this lesson you will consider how important it is for a Christian to relate to others as a servant. A person who serves God well has certain qualities in his or her life. Those qualities will be discussed. You will discuss ways to be of service, including specific applications in your own life.

1. Begin the study by spending a few minutes reviewing the Scripture memory assignment for this lesson, as well as verses from previous lessons.
2. Discuss responses to Question 1. Do you see a great difference between service from the Christian community and service from those who are not Christians?
3. As you discuss Question 2, some in the group may be willing to share how they react to serving others. Is it difficult, particularly in certain circumstances?
4. Consider John 13:14-17 (Question 3). Jesus washed the disciples' feet, then said that a servant is no greater than the one he serves. Does that apply to Jesus as well?
5. Discuss responses to Question 4. Have you observed in yourself or in others an act of service in which the servant looked down on those whom he served? Is that servanthood? Should servanthood reach into

79

some areas of our life more than others, or should it be a consideration moment by moment?

6. Discuss Paul's attitude toward serving others (Question 5).
7. How could 2 Corinthians 4:5 (Question 6) be applied through what we say? How could it be applied through what we do?
8. Share responses to Question 7. Is one kind of serving any more valuable than the other?
9. Discuss the characteristics of a servant (Question 9). Could a person be an effective servant if one of these qualities was missing? How realistic is it to find these qualities today?
10. Those who wish to, can share their thoughts concerning Question 10. Some in the group may be able to compare their attitude toward serving before and after they became a Christian.
11. Give an opportunity for questions or suggestions for the personal project.
12. Pray that those present will apply what they have learned concerning servanthood.

NOTES FROM YOUR GROUP DISCUSSION

THE MINISTRY
OF GIVING

Review the following verses, and check them off after quoting them correctly from memory.

Matthew 28:18-20 ___   Proverbs 1:5, 7 ___
Jeremiah 29:11 ___   Titus 2:11-12 ___
Psalm 27:8 ___   2 Timothy 3:16-17 ___
1 Corinthians 9:16 ___   1 Thessalonians 5:12-13 ___
1 John 1:3 ___   2 Corinthians 4:5 ___

Scripture Memory Assignment: Luke 6:38

1. Read 2 Corinthians 8:7 and 9, and 9:8 and 11. What does God teach through Paul about the ministry of giving?

   _____

   _____

   _____

   _____

   _____

   _____

2. What motivation for giving do you find in the following verses?

Proverbs 19:17

_____

_____

Matthew 6:19-20

_____

_____

_____

Hebrews 6:10

_____

_____

3. For each verse or passage below, write a word or phrase which describes how we should give.

1 Chronicles 29:9

_____

1 Chronicles 29:17

_____

Psalm 37:21

_____

Matthew 6:1,3-4

_____

2 Corinthians 8:2-3

_____

2 Corinthians 8:12

_____

2 Corinthians 9:7

_____

Romans 12:13

_____

4. Which verse or passage in Question 3 points to your strength in giving?

_____

Which verse or passage points to your weakness?

_____

5. What does God promise to those who will give to him and his work? Read Malachi 3:10-11, Proverbs 11:24-25, Luke 6:38, 2 Corinthians 9:6, and Philippians 4:18-19.

_____

_____

_____

_____

_____

_____

6. What results when God's people give? Read 2 Corinthians 9:12-14.

_____

_____

_____

_____

7. Giving can be done in ways that do not involve money. What example do you find in Luke 14:12-14?

_____

_____

_____

8. To whom should we give, whether it is money or time or service?

Haggai 1:6-9

_____

_____

Galatians 6:6

_____

_____

1 Peter 4:9

_____

_____

James 2:15-16

_____

_____

9. Read Malachi 3:8.

   a. A tithe is 10%. Are you giving at least 11% on a regular basis?

   _____

   b. What can you do to begin giving 11%, or to increase your giving beyond that portion?

   _____

   _____

   _____

10. How do you or could you apply to your giving the principle expressed in:

    1 Corinthians 16:2

    _____

    _____

    _____

    2 Corinthians 8:11-12

    _____

    _____

    _____

_____

_____

_____

11. In Question 4 you were asked to give some thought to your strengths and weaknesses in giving. Have you become aware of other needs concerning your giving? What can you do to correct them?

_____

_____

_____

_____

Personal Project: If you are not doing so, find a Christian worker, project, or organization to support. You will have a direct involvement in the ministry, whether it is in your country or another nation.

Questions for Group Discussion
The purpose of this lesson on giving is to realize without question that every Christian has a responsibility to give some of his resources back to God. It will become obvious that a Christian will not be able to give without receiving blessings in return. God has provided some guidelines concerning how much to give, how to give it, and to whom.

1. Review the Scripture memory assignment.
2. Discuss Question 1. How much should we be willing to give? Describe the grace of giving which Christ showed. From whom do we receive what we give to others?

3. According to Matthew 6:19-20 (Question 2), we will be rewarded in heaven for giving today. What other reasons motivate you to give?
4. Share responses to Question 3. What is a practical application of each verse or passage? Use your imagination. According to 2 Corinthians 9:7, what is as important to God as the gift we give?
5. Question 4 is an excellent opportunity for those in the group to share experiences in which they have given and received more than they gave in return.
6. Discuss responses to Question 5.
7. What other means of giving (Question 6) can you suggest, with a scriptural basis if possible?
8. Answer Question 7 together. To whom should the first portion of our gift money go? What personal guidelines have you developed to help you make decisions about how to distribute your money?
9. Read Malachi 3:8-9 (Question 8). What was the effect of not faithfully returning to God a share of his provision?
10. How could the principles discussed for Question 9 apply to other means of giving, such as time and talent?
11. Some in the group may have difficulty answering Question 10. What advice or suggestions can you share to encourage others to give on a regular basis or to increase what they give?
12. The personal project is an opportunity for those in the group to share and help meet a need they may be aware of. Information can be shared about an individual, a project, or an organization.
13. The time spent in prayer might focus on thanking God for the resources he has made available to each person.

NOTES FROM YOUR GROUP DISCUSSION

THE FRUIT
OF THE SPIRIT

Review the following verses, and check them off after quoting them correctly from memory.

Matthew 28:18-20 ___   Proverbs 1:5, 7 ___
Jeremiah 29:11 ___   Titus 2:11-12 ___
Psalm 27:8 ___   2 Timothy 3:16-17 ___
1 Corinthians 9:16 ___   1 Thessalonians 5:12-13 ___
1 John 1:3 ___   2 Corinthians 4:5 ___
Luke 6:38 ___

Scripture Memory Assignment: Galatians 5:22-23

1. Read Galatians 5:22-23.

   a. List each fruit of the Spirit and define or describe it.

   _____

   _____

   _____

   _____

   _____

_____

_____

_____

_____

_____

_____

_____

_____

_____

_____

_____

_____

b. For each fruit listed, try to think of a circumstance in which you exhibit that fruit consistently. Also describe a circumstance in which you find it difficult to exhibit that fruit.

_____

_____

_____

_____

_____

_____

_____

_____

_____

_____

_____

_____

_____

_____

_____

_____

2. 1 Corinthians 13:4-7 describes the love we are to show. Choose one relationship that involves love, such as parent and child. Describe how each characteristic of love could be applied to the relationship.

_____

3. Paraphrase the passage in John 15:2-8.

_____

_____

_____

_____

_____

_____

4. What does Hebrews 12:11 teach about John 15:2-8?

_____

_____

_____

_____

_____

5. Read Matthew 7:20, Romans 13:14, Philippians 1:11, and 2 Peter 1:5-8. Why is it important for a Christian to show the fruit of the Spirit?

_____

_____

_____

_____

_____

6. How can each of the qualities listed in 2 Peter 1:5-7 become a part of the life of a Christian?

_____

_____

_____

_____

_____

_____

_____

_____

7. According to 1 Peter 2:20-23, what is one way in which we can show evidence of the fruit of the Spirit?

_____

_____

_____

_____

8. Which fruit of the Spirit do you most need to develop as a Christian? Choose one or two and make specific plans to do so.

_____

_____

_____

_____

Personal Project: It can be difficult to try to take more than one step of growth at a time. Look over the personal project you described for each lesson in this book. Choose the one you feel is the most important need you have at the moment. You may want to put all the projects in order of priority. Accomplish one before you go on to the next. For Lesson 12, you might consider Question 6 as the personal project.

_____

_____

_____

_____

_____

_____

_____

_____

_____

_____

_____

Questions for Group Discussion
This concluding lesson will reveal what the fruit of the Spirit is according to Scripture. It should become obvious that this fruit should be a visible part of our life, attractive enough to draw others to Christ. The study and discussion will bring out ways in which to develop the fruit of the Spirit.

1. Review of the Scripture memory assignment will lead very easily into discussion of the first question in the study.
2. As you discuss Question 1, part a, take time to develop a group definition of each fruit listed. Why is the term *fruit* used in this context? How would you interpret and apply the last sentence in verse 23?
3. If those in the group are willing, discuss Question 1, part b, by asking which fruit are the easiest and which are the most difficult to manifest. What do you think the reasons are?
4. Read 1 Corinthians 13:4-7 aloud before you discuss Question 2. What relationship did each person in the group consider as they followed the directions? How could patient love be applied to a relationship between brother and sister, or between a wife and her father-in-law? What should we do when we fail to love as we should? What are the implications of living a life of love today?
5. Share and discuss several paraphrases of John 15:2-8 (Question 3). What thought in the passage impressed you the most? How can we remain in Jesus?
6. Discuss Question 4. What are some examples of painful but profitable discipline?
7. Share responses to Question 5. What does it mean to be effective and productive in our knowledge of Jesus Christ? How does Peter's list compare with Paul's list in Galatians? Why do you think they are different?
8. Discuss Question 6. Be as specific as possible in suggesting ways to develop the qualities or fruit listed in the passage. Do you think the order of the qualities is important? Why do you think love is last?
9. Answer Question 7. Which fruit would be evident through an experience such as that described in 1 Peter 2:20-23? Have you or someone you know been through such an experience? What was the outcome?
10. Give an opportunity for those who are willing to share their responses to Question 8. How does your response to Christ's lordship affect your application of this lesson?

11. The personal project suggested in this lesson involves the projects from all the other lessons. Some of those in the group may find it difficult to decide which project deserves their attention first. If they are willing to share their needs, help them make a decision about what to do first. The way in which others see us can be very helpful.
12. As you close the study with prayer, give thanks for what has been learned in this lesson as well as the entire study on discipleship. Ask for wisdom and perseverance in applying God's word.

NOTES FROM YOUR GROUP DISCUSSION